GW00674277

Invitation to Madrigals 5

A second selection of four-part works
transcribed and edited by
THURSTON DART
for SATB

Stainer & Bell

© 1971 Stainer & Bell Ltd
23 Gruneisen Road, London N3 1DZ

ISBN 0 85249 208 1

CONTENTS

———————o———————

FOREWORD

THE MADRIGAL was an invention of 14th-century Italy. Laid aside during the whole of the 15th century, it was taken up again in a new form about 1530 and it remained in favour for another hundred years. No one knows when English musicians first began to sing Italian madrigals, but by 1588 their vogue had become sufficiently great for Nicholas Yonge, a choirman of St. Paul's Cathedral, to issue his famous *Musica Transalpina*. This was a selection of madrigals for four, five and six voices, composed by the leading Italian musicians of the time, together with two stanzas from Ariosto set by William Byrd (1543–1623). Ariosto's poems, like all the others in the collection, were translated into English for Yonge's publication—"brought to speak English", as the title-page puts it.

Despite Byrd's essays in the new Italian style, the ordinary musical language used by most English composers of his generation was not in the least Italian, as we can tell from such books as Byrd's own *Psalmes, Sonets & Songs* (1588), issued a few months before Yonge's collection, his *Songs of Sundrie Natures* (1589), or Mundy's *Songs and Psalmes* (1594). The poems found in these collections are ungainly and harsh to the ear, the metres jog-trot, the counterpoint rugged, and the harmony restless. Slowly at first and then more compellingly, the elegance and balance of the Italian style took hold of the English imagination in poetry as in music, and moralizing rhymes gave way to sugared sonnets. The publication of Watson's *Italian Madrigalls Englished* (1590) gave momentum to the new trend in music, but the composers of this collection were Italians to a man. The true English madrigal was created almost single-handed by Thomas Morley (c. 1558–1602?), chiefly through a sequence of music-books published between 1593 and 1597 containing madrigals, canzonets, balletts, and fantasies of his own composition. The sequence was rounded off with a collection of 4-part canzonets by Italian composers, and a masterly treatise including rules for composing in the newer Italian style—Morley's famous *A Plaine and Easie Introduction to Practicall Musicke* (1597). The music in these books ranged from two-part to seven-part writing (the limits maintained by nearly all the English madrigalists), and the books were an instant success. In the short space of four years Morley had successfully grafted on to an English stock almost every shoot of the Italian madrigal: the madrigal proper, the canzonet, the ballett, the pastoral, the wordless fantasia. Classical in their simplicity, smooth-running in their words, fresh in harmony and counterpoint, Morley's madrigalian writings were models for a whole generation of his friends, colleagues and pupils. The astonishing flowering of the English madrigal during the next thirty years was very largely due to the skill, taste, enterprise and discernment of this one remarkable musician.

The life's work of another remarkable musician, the late Dr Edmund H. Fellowes, has made the riches of this school of English composers known to countless thousands of music-lovers throughout the world. But few madrigals are simple to perform at first sight, and the present book is planned as a sequel to *Invitation to Madrigals*, 2—a plain and easy introduction to practical madrigal-singing, for soprano, alto, tenor and bass. The madrigals and other works it contains have been newly transcribed and edited from the original sources, and they have been arranged in increasing order of difficulty.

iv

For each piece I have added a few notes on rehearsal and performance. The collection illustrates the variety of styles current between 1590 and 1625. All of the pieces in the collection were originally composed as quartets, though I have had to make a few transpositions and slight adaptations of the musical texture, to keep within the normal ranges of present-day amateur voices. I have done my best to keep these changes as few as possible, and I have also tried to make them conform to Elizabethan and Jacobean custom.

Madrigals are epigrammatic poems, set as vocal chamber-music; that is to say, they are sung to perfection when there is no more than one voice to a part. Their revival in our own time has shown what enjoyment they can also bring to groups of singers, and all the pieces in this book can sound well when performed by small choirs. The individual voices, like the four vocal parts, should be well balanced among themselves. Whispering the words to the musical rhythms will help with problems of phrasing, stressing, enunciation and meaning. Stressed notes will usually be those that are a little longer or higher than their neighbours. Bar-lines have been put in for convenience, not necessarily to show stress. The original Elizabethan and Jacobean part-books are unbarred, and they contain no dynamics or tempo marks. Each singer was evidently expected to make up his own mind about interpretation, rather than to accept other people's ready-made opinions. High-pitched notes and phrases must not be allowed to cry down the other parts; low notes and phrases should not be too submerged. The words must always be clear, and the tone-colour and dynamics of the music should match the verbal sense as closely as glove fits hand. To encourage performers to be adventurous in their interpretations, I have omitted almost all indications of dynamics, tempo and phrasing.

In Armada year, when the true English madrigal was still unborn, Byrd wrote "there is not any music of instruments whatsoever, comparable to that which is made of the voices of men, where the voices are good, and the same well sorted and ordered.

> Since singing is so good a thing,
> I wish all men would learn to sing."

Byrd's most distinguished pupil, Thomas Morley, made the English madrigal, so he is entitled to have the last word about it. In his treatise of 1597 Morley wrote "The best kind of [light music] is termed Madrigal . . . a kind of music made upon songs and sonnets, such as Petrarch and many poets of our time have excelled in . . . As for the music, it is—next unto the Motet—the most artificial, and to men of understanding most delightful . . . You must possess yourself with an amorous humour . . . so that you must in your music be wavering like the wind, sometimes wanton, sometimes drooping, sometimes grave and staid, otherwhile effeminate . . . and the more variety you show the better shall you please". These were hints to would-be composers, but they still remain the best of guides for performers of these enchanting works.

King's College,   THURSTON DART
*London, W.C.*2

① Love shooting

RICHARD DERING (1620)

Love shoot-ing a - mong ma - ny, By chance he hit not

Love shooting a - mong ma - ny, By chance he hit not

Love shoot - ing a - mong ma - ny, By chance he hit not

Love shoot - ing a - mong ma - ny, By chance he hit not

a - ny, by chance he hit not a - ny.

a - ny, by chance he hit not a - - - ny.

a - ny, by chance he hit not a - ny.

a - ny, by chance he hit not a - ny.

Lo! then the shaft re - bound- ed, lo! _____ then the shaft re -

Lo! then the shaft re - bound- ed, lo! then the shaft re -

Lo! then the shaft re - bound- ed, lo! _____ then the shaft re -

Lo! then the shaft re - bound- ed, lo! _____ then the shaft re -

Dering and Philips spent nearly all their working lives abroad, and their madrigals were published
 Antwerp. This canzonet originally had Italian words ('Tutta gentile e bella'); I have adapted some
'om Farnaby's 13th canzonet. For the original text, see Musica Britannica, XXV (Dering's complete
ecular music, much of it of great beauty and originality).

② Thus saith my Cloris bright

JOHN WILBYE (1598)

8

A madrigal in a pure 16th-century style. Beat slow minims. The short bar-lines, like the long ones, are only for co-ordinating the parts, and the less they are perceived the better. Don't let the s's be too prominent.

③ A satyr once

JOHN WARD (1613)

A sa - tyr once ___ did run ___ a - way, did

A sa - tyr, a sa - tyr once did run ___ a -

A sa - tyr once ___ did run, did run ___ a-

run ___ a - way, did run a - way for dread,

way, did run ___ a - way for ___ dread,

way, did run ___ a - way At sound of

for dread,

At sound of horn, at sound of ___ horn which

At sound of horn, at sound of horn, sound of

horn, at sound of horn, at sound of horn, at sound of horn which

At sound of horn, at sound of horn which

f

Deem - ing strange e - - - vil,

f

e - vil, deem - ing strange e - - -

fled he ___ fled, *f* Deem-

fled, Deem - ing strange

deem - ing strange e - vil, deem - ing

vil, strange e - vil, deem - ing strange e - -

- ing strange e - vil ___ in ___

e - - - vil, deem - ing strange e - - -

1. **2.**

strange e - vil in that he did not know. know.

p

- vil in that he did not know. Fear - ing and know.

that he did ___ not know. know.

vil in that he did not know. ___ know.

)rds by Sir Philip Sidney. Ward is perhaps more at home in writing in more parts, since this allows
•more scope for unexpected rich suspensions. I've exchanged a few notes of the T. and B. in bars
10, for convenience of tessitura.
S. and Λ. are equal in range; their parts should be interchanged at the repeats.

④ What poor astronomers JOHN DOWLAND (1603)

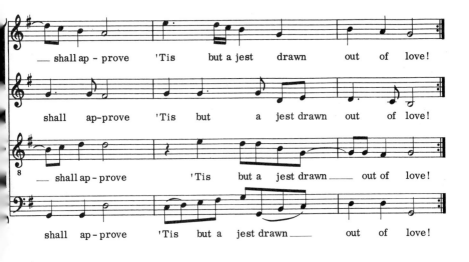

shall ap - prove 'Tis but a jest drawn out of love!

shall ap-prove 'Tis but a jest drawn out of love!

shall ap - prove 'Tis but a jest drawn out of love!

shall ap - prove 'Tis but a jest drawn out of love!

2 And love itself is but a jest,
Devis'd by idle heads,
To catch young fancies in the nest
And lay it in fools' beds;
That, being hatch'd in beauty's eyes,
They may be fledg'd ere they be wise.

3 But yet it is a sport to see
How wit will run on wheels,
While will cannot persuaded be
With that which reason feels:
That women's eyes and stars are odd
And love is but a feigned god.

4 But such as will run mad with will
I cannot clear their sight,
But leave them to their study still
To look where is no light.
Till time too late we make them try,
They study false astronomy.

An ayre for four voices, or for voice and lute, or voice and viols, or what you will. The small notes in the S. at bar 3 are taken from the lute part and may be added by those who find the texture incomplete without them. Keep the lower voices somewhat subdued throughout, for several pleasing irregularities in the part-writing show that the ayre was originally conceived as an accompanied solo song.

⑤ Lo country sports

THOMAS WEELKES (1597)

have the— prize; Then all at once for our town cries, then all at

the prize; Then all at once for our town

prize, the —— prize; Then all at once for our town cries, then all at

—— prize; Then all at once for our town

once for our town cries, all —— for our town cries; Pipe on for

cries, then all at once for our town cries, then all at once for our town

once for our town cries; Pipe on for we will have the prize, we'll have the——

cries, then all at once for our town cries; Pipe on for we will have the

we will have the prize, for we —— will have the prize.

cries; pipe on for we will have the prize.

—— prize, pipe on for we will have—— the—— prize.

prize, pipe on for we will have the —— prize.

his should chime like morris dancers' bells. Let the answering phrases (S. and A., T. and B.) arefully balanced in loudness. The rare chromatics ought to be used to colour the diatonic harmony, the quavers must point the rather four-square rhythms.

⑥ Round about in a fair ring

JOHN BENNET (1614

Round a - bout, round a - bout in a fair ring-a,

Round a - bout, round a - bout in a fair ring-a,

Round a - bout, round a - bout in a fair ring - a,

Round a - bout, round a - bout in a fair ring-a,

Thus we dance, thus we dance, and thus we sing - a:

Thus we dance, thus we dance, and thus we sing - a:

Thus we dance, thus we dance, and thus we sing - a:

Thus we dance, thus we dance, and thus we sing - a:

Trip & trip & go, to & fro & fro,

Trip & trip & go, to &

Trip & trip & go,

Trip & trip & go, to & fro &

to & fro, to & fro,

fro & fro, to & to & fro,

to & fro & fro, & fro,

fro, to & to & fro, & fro,

o - ver this green - a. All a - bout, in & out, all a -bout,

o - ver this green - a. All a - bout, in & out, all a -bout,

o - ver this green - a. All a - bout, in & out, all a -bout,

o - ver this green - a. All a - bout, in & out, all a -bout,

in & out, all a - bout, in & out o - ver this green-a.

in & out, all a - bout, in & out o - ver this green - a.

in & out, all a - bout, in & out o - ver this green - a.

in & out, all a - bout, in & out o - ver this green - a.

A song ('The Elves Dance') from Ravenscroft's treatise, and very different in style from Bennet's madrigals of 1599. Perhaps composed for a choirboy play; sing as lightly and delicately as possible.

⑦ If love be blind

THOMAS BATESON (1604)

The pattering quavers need attention; and the music can sound rather lumpy, so try to make it clear in texture and freely flowing, with some judicious rubato in the beat.

⑧ In ev'ry place

THOMAS MORLEY (1594)

26

The opening points of imitation are drawn from Lassus's famous chanson, 'Suzanne un jour';
Morley's words, too, seem related to the story of Susannah and the Elders.

This thoughtful, elegiac madrigal is as typical of Morley as his light canzonets, though in discussion
we often overlook this side of him. It needs great precision and eloquence throughout, in both words
and music.

⑨ Wherefore sit I complaining?

PETER PHILIPS (1591)

much, mine eyes, shall dear-ly buy— it.

saw too much, that saw too much, mine eyes, shall dear-ly buy

you that saw too much, mine eyes, shall dear-ly buy

saw too much, mine eyes, shall dear - ly, shall dear-ly buy

Still thus to weep— for e - ver Your foun-tains shall per-se -

it. Still thus to weep— for e - ver Your foun-tains shall per-se -

it. Still thus to weep— for e - ver Your foun-tains shall per-se -

it. Still thus to weep— for e - ver You

ver, your foun - tains shall— per-se -

ver, your foun - tains, your foun - tains shall— per-se -

ver, your foun - tains, your foun - tains shall— per-se -

foun - tains shall per-se - ver,

ver, O eyes that did ___ e - spy it, that did e - spy___

ver, O eyes that did ___ e - spy it, that did e - spy

ver, O eyes that did ___ e - spy it, that did e - spy___

O eyes that did ___ e - spy it, that did e - spy

it. False com - fort, hence, for thou canst ne - ver

it False com - fort, hence, for thou canst ne - ver ease___

it. False

it. False com -

ease me, false com - fort, hence, for thou canst

me, false com - fort, hence, for thou canst ne-ver ease me,

com - fort, hence,_ for thou canst ne-ver ease me,

fort, hence, for thou canst ne-ver ease me, hence, for thou canst

Originally, like Dering's canzonet, a setting of Italian words in a fully madrigalian style
Voi volete ch'io muoia'); I have adapted some from Morley's 3rd, 4th and 19th madrigals of 1594.
▸r the original text, see Musica Britannica, XXIX (a fine selection of Philips's Italian madrigals
▸ 4, 5, 6 and 8 voices).

(10) **Change me, O heav'ns**　　　JOHN WILBYE (1609)

In Wilbye's mature style, full of delicious tonal ambiguities and surprising turns of phrase.
Sing as flexibly and imaginatively as possible: words, *words*, WORDS!
Leaps of a major sixth are notoriously difficult to sing in tune.......

(II) # O let me live

THOMAS TOMKINS (1622)

la la la   la   la,   fa la   la   la la la,

fa   la   la la la,   fa la la   la,   fa   la

Fa   la la la la,   fa la la la la,   fa

la,   fa   la,   fa la la   la,   fa   la la la la,

fa   la   la la la,   fa la la____ la la   la

la la la,   fa la la____ la   la,   fa   la   la   la la

la   la,   fa____ la   la,   fa   la   la   la

fa la la   la,   fa   la   la,   fa   la   la   la

la,   fa la   la   la   la,   fa   la   la la la.   O__ la.

la,fa la   la   la____ la la,   fa la la,   fa la la la   la.   la.

la,   fa la la la____ la la,   fa   la la la   la.   la.

la,   fa la   la   la   la,   fa   la la la   la.   la.

omkins called his pieces 'Songs', not madrigals; many of them can serve to illustrate how the strict
rigal genre decayed into a hotch-potch drawn from the lute-song, the ballett, the madrigal, the
onet, and even from keyboard music (e.g., those strange leaps in the B.).

h song is dedicated to a different friend; this one is for Dr (John) Dowland, and calls for a slow,
ained, bitter-sweet style.   You may find it best to begin with crotchet beats.

eep within the normal compasses, I have interchanged A. and T. for a few bars in the 2nd section.

(12) **Blind Love**

GILES FARNABY (1598)

And tra-cing forth his foot - ing His

And tra-cing forth his foot - - - - ing His

tra-cing,tra-cing forth, and tracing forth his foot - ing

And tra-cing forth his foot - - - ing

mo - ther Ve - nus spied it, Be-fore

— mo-ther Ve- nus, his mo - ther Ve - nus spied it, Be-fore

His mo - ther Ve - nus, his mo-ther Venus spied it, Be-fore

His mo - ther Ve - nus spied it,

the boy could hide it.

— the boy, be - fore the boy could hide it.

— the boy, be - fore the boy could hide it. 1. (And)

Be-fore the boy could hide it.

'he ambiguous tonality goes well with the words; I hesitated whether to use a key-signature of 4 flats, decided against it. The T. underlay has been slightly adjusted; Farnaby's is often hit-or-miss.

(13) **Take time**

JOHN FARMER (1599)

An experimental song, in which the T. sings nothing but the notes of the hexachord (ut re mi fa sol la : *Invitation to Madrigals*, Bk. 4, pp. 8-10), in an arbitrary sequence of note-values.
bring these out, I've omitted bar-lines in the T. The moralizing words, like the artificial construction
he music, link this piece to the pre-madrigalian style of Whythorne, Tallis and Byrd.

(14) Construe my meaning

GILES FARNABY (1598)

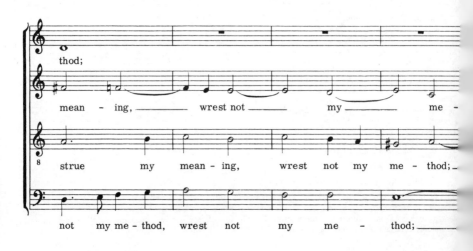

Con - strue my ____ mean-ing, ____ wrest not my

Con - strue my ____ mean-ing, ____

me - thod, ____ wrest ____ not my ____ me -

Con - strue my

____ wrest not my me - thod, con -

Con - strue my mean - ing, wrest

thod;

mean - ing, ____ wrest not ____ my ____ me -

strue my mean - ing, wrest not my me - thod;

not my me - thod, wrest not my me - thod; ____

justly admired chromatic madrigal, as difficult to sing in tune as some of Gesualdo's (and, like his, ~~h~~aps composed at a harmony instrument). It is likely that Farnaby was a joiner and virginals-maker ~~p~~rofession, and in religion he was devoutly low church. His touching words to this madrigal seem a ~~~~ of apologia for what he considered might be his shortcomings as a polyphonic composer.

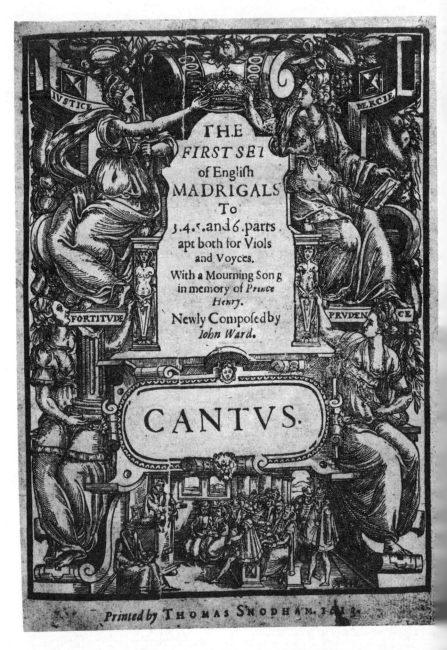

THE
FIRST SET
of English
MADRIGALS
To
3. 4. 5. and 6. parts.
apt both for Viols
and Voyces.

With a Mourning Song
in memory of *Prince*
Henry.

Newly Composed by
Iohn Ward.

JUSTICE MERCIE

FORTITVDE PRVDENCE

CANTVS.

Printed by THOMAS SNODHAM. 1613.

The original decorated titlepage for John Ward's madrigal collection (*see* **3**). Althou[gh]
named "the first" it was Ward's only publication. The woodblock used was then over fo[rty]
years old: originally Queen Elizabeth I was shown being crowned by Justice and Mer[cy.]
Fortitude and Prudence now support the sides of a vanished throne.